Chancing it

Acknowledgements

Cover design: Oliver Heath, Rafters Design

All illustrations apart from page 23 ©Paul Gardiner, 2005. The right of Paul Gardiner to be identified as the illustrator of this work has been asserted by him in accordance with the Copyright, Design and Patents Act, 1988.

Brinsford books are a direct result of the findings of a two-year authoring/research project with young offenders at HMYOI Brinsford, near Wolverhampton. Grateful thanks go to all the young people who participated so enthusiastically in the project and to Judy Jackson and Brian Eccleshall of Dudley College of Technology.

First published in Great Britain by Axis Education Ltd

ISBN 1-903685-95-8

Axis Education PO Box 459
Shrewsbury SY4 4WZ

Email: enquiries@axiseducation.co.uk

www.axiseducation.co.uk

It was dark.

Pete and Robby went down the road. No one saw them.

There were only cars in the road. Cars do not
see you.

Pete stopped. He saw a bike.

Robby saw it too.

"That's a tatty bike," said Robby.

"No," said Pete. "It is a great bike. It's an RD350.
They go mega fast."

The bike just sat there in the drive.

"I want it," said Pete.

It was the best.

"What about the man that owns it?" said Robby. "If you get nicked again you will go to jail this time."

"I will not get caught," said Pete. "If I do, it will be another judge. Or the last one will forget what he said."

"It is not worth it," said Robby. "If you nick it I don't want nothing to do with it. I'm not gonna go down."
And he ran away from Pete.

Pete did not care what Robby said. He could wire the bike.
He would be long gone when the man woke up.
He liked taking chances.

Pete took out his tools. The job did not take long.
No one saw him.
There was even a crash hat in the back box!

Pete went down the drive on the bike. He was on the road.
He felt cool!

"Wow! It's fast! It goes like shit off a shovel!"
Pete felt the wind on his face.

The bike went faster and faster.
But he did not want to go too fast. The pigs might pick him up.

He drove to the old factory. Four of his mates were there.
Danny said, “What a tatty old bike. And it smokes!”

"It is a two stroke, stupid," said Pete. "They all smoke a bit. It can go real fast. Let me show you." He shot onto the big field by the old factory.

Pete went to the far end of the field. He made the bike lean over to go faster.

“Wow! Look at him go!” said Danny.
His mates ran up the field.
“Give us a go. Go on!”

“Get stuffed,” said Pete. “You can all have a backy.
No one rides it but me, okay?”
“Okay. Who is first?”

They took turns. Two and three up. Then the bike died. It was Danny's turn next.

"It is a load of crap," he said. "We should burn it."

“No way,” said Pete. “It has only run out of gas.”
But he had no cash.
He would have to wait a day or two.

“Just as well,” said Robby.
We are too close to that man.
“He will see it if you go on it.”

"I will paint it – then no one will know," said Pete.
"Then I can ride it when I want."

Robby came to help him paint the bike.
"You sure you want to keep it?" he said.
"The owner is only round the corner."

"I must keep it," said Pete. "If I paint it red, he will not know. I want to ride on the road. A field is not the same."

They made the bike red.
Even the crash hat was red.
Pete was proud of his work.

He got money from his Mum for gas.
"Come on," said Pete.
They took the bike out.

"Not that way!" said Robby.
"Why not?"
"It goes past his house."

"It is now or never," said Pete.
"Are you mad?" said Robby.

Robby hung on to the back of the bike.
They went round the corner.
Robby saw the man at the end of his drive.

But the man did not see that the red bike was his.
He did not move. He did not shout.
They had done it!

The bike had to have more gas.
"Got any dosh?" said Pete.
"No. I am broke," said Robby.
"We cannot ride it till my giro comes," said Pete.

Danny and the rest ran into the factory.
"We are going to Blackpool. Want to come?
The rides at the fair! The beach! All those girls!
It will be great."

"I am skint," said Pete. "I cannot go."

"Nor me," said Robby.

"You must come," said Danny. "It will not be the same."

Pete had an idea.

"I could sell the bike," he said.

"We will have a great time. Blackpool here we come!"

They had a great time in Blackpool.
Pete spent a lot of money.
"A hundred quid! Bloody hell! I have spent a hundred quid! In one day!"

Pete gave his mates a grin.
“It has been great! Those girls we met on the beach.
Pity we cannot do it all again.”

“Yeah. It will be dead boring now,” said Robby.
“None of us has got a penny. And you have not
got the bike.”

"That bike was great," said Pete. "It was tatty. But it went fast. I wish I still had it. I think I will get it back."

"Are you mad?" said Robby. "You know who you sold it to. It will be bad if you nick it back. He has hard fists. You would really be chancing it."

"I never said I would nick it back. I will buy it back."
"How long will it take you to save all that dosh?" said Robby.

"Too long," said Pete. "You are right. I want that bike back, and soon. I will get it somehow.
Just you wait and see."

Glossary

Blackpool	a seaside town in the northwest of England
corner	the point where two roads meet
factory	a building where machines are used to make large amounts of products
field	land used for playing sport, keeping animals or growing crops
giro	money from the government for someone who is unemployed, ill or who has a very low income
judge	the person in charge of a crown court case who decides how criminals should be punished